DISNEP PRINCESS

POCAHONTAS

LEVEL 6

Re-told by: Andy Hopkins
Series Editor: Melanie Williams

Pearson Education Limited
Edinburgh Gate, Harlow,
Essex CM20 2JE, England
and Associated Companies throughout the world.

ISBN: 978-1-4082-8874-0

This edition first published by Pearson Education Ltd. 2013

5 7 9 10 8 6 4

Text copyright © Pearson Education Ltd. 2013
Copyright © 2013 Disney Enterprises, Inc. All rights reserved.

The moral rights of the author have been asserted
in accordance with the Copyright Designs and Patents Act 1988

Set in 15/19pt OT Fiendstar
Printed in China
SWTC/04

Published by Pearson Education Ltd.

For a complete list of the titles available in the Pearson English Kids Readers series, please go to
www.pearsonenglishkidsreaders.com. Alternatively, write to your local Pearson Education office or to
Pearson English Readers Marketing Department, Pearson Education, Edinburgh Gate, Harlow, Essex CM202JE, England.

It was a beautiful spring morning in 1607. John Smith was on a new ship. He loved the ocean. He was excited about traveling again from England to the new land for more adventures. The sailors were excited, too. There were a lot of stories about the new land. There was gold everywhere! The sailors wanted to get rich and find a better life.

"Is that him?" asked Thomas, a young sailor. "I've heard a lot of stories about him."

"Yes, that's John Smith," answered another sailor. "He's a good sailor, brave and fair."

John Smith's ship was carrying an important passenger, a rich man called Ratcliffe.

"Go to the new land," King James ordered Ratcliffe. "Discover a new place and bring me back gold and silver. Call the place Jamestown. It will be part of England."

The ship left London and sailed toward the open ocean. There were shouts from the crowd, "Good luck!" and "Come back soon!" Everyone seemed happy. But John Smith knew the dangers of journeys to new lands. A few days later, far out in the ocean, the ship sailed into a storm.

Heavy rain fell from the black sky and there was a strong wind. Big waves hit the ship. Suddenly, Thomas fell. A very big wave threw him into the water.

John Smith saw it happen. "I'm coming!" he shouted. He quickly put a rope around himself and jumped into the water after Thomas. "Hold on to me."

Smith put his strong arm around the young sailor. Thomas's clothes were heavy with water. It was difficult to hold him.

"Pull us in!" Smith shouted to the others. Slowly, the sailors pulled the two men back onto the ship.

"Thank you, Smith," said Thomas. "You saved my life. I'll always remember that."

The storm worried the sailors — Ratcliffe could see that. "Don't worry, men," he told them. "Soon we will be in the new land. You will be free there — you will be rich! You are the best sailors in England. If we meet Indians, we will defeat them. No one can stop us!"

"This new land is going to be great, John," said Thomas later. "I'm going to find a lot of gold, and build a big house. If anyone tries to stop me, I'll shoot."

In the new land, Chief Powhatan spoke to his people. "We have defeated our enemy in the north and saved our villages," he said. "Our friends have helped us, and we thank them."

"The people are happy again, Chief Powhatan," said old Kekata. "Look at all their smiling faces."

"Yes, but where is the smiling face of my daughter, Pocahontas? Where is she?"

Kekata smiled. "You know Pocahontas. She has her mother's spirit. She follows the wind: it takes her here and there, along the river, through the forest, into the mountains."

Pocahontas stood on a mountaintop with the wind against her face. She could feel the spirits of the forest with her. She loved this land.

"Pocahontas! Pocahontas!" A voice came from far away. She looked down. It was her friend Nakoma.

"Pocahontas! Your father is home. Come down here."

Her father was back! Pocahontas was very happy. Then she jumped off a rock into the lake far below and came up near her friend's boat. She spit some water at Nakoma and laughed.

"Aren't we too old for these games?" Nakoma smiled.

"What were you doing up there?" asked Nakoma.

"I was thinking about my dream again. I know it means something."

They went back to the village. Chief Powhatan saw his daughter and smiled. "Pocahontas! It's good to see you. Come with me. There's a lot to talk about."

They sat down.

"Kocoum is the bravest fighter of all our men," the Chief said. "He fights with the power of a bear."

"He's a very strong man," Pocahontas agreed.

"What do you think of him, my daughter?" asked her father.

Pocahontas did not want to talk about Kocoum. She wanted to ask her father about her dream.

"Father," Pocahontas began, "I often have a dream. I think it's telling me something. Something is going to happen."

"Something *is* going to happen, my child," Chief Powhatan said. "Kocoum wants to marry you."

"Kocoum? But Father ..."

"Kocoum will be a good husband. He will look after you."

"But Father, my dream. I think I have to take another path."

"Listen, Pocahontas. You are the Chief's daughter. You must take your place with our people."

He gave her a necklace. "This was your mother's necklace. She wanted you to wear it at your wedding."

Pocahontas went to the forest. "Grandmother Willow, Father wants me to marry Kocoum!"

"And you don't want to marry him?"

"My father thinks it's the right path for me. But I often have a dream. I'm in the forest. There's an arrow in front of me. It starts to move around and around. And then, suddenly, it stops."

"Well, perhaps the arrow is showing you your path."

"But what *is* my path, Grandmother Willow?"

"All around you are spirits, in the earth, in the water, in the sky. Listen to them. Listen with your heart. You will find your path."

Pocahontas closed her eyes and listened. At first, there was nothing. Then, slowly, she began to hear the spirits of the forest. She could smell animals and leaves and flowers. She could almost taste the water in the river. Then she began to see a picture in her head.

"I can see something!" She opened her eyes and climbed to the top of a tree.

"What do you see, child?" asked Grandmother Willow.

Pocahontas could not say. She was looking out at the ocean. Her mouth and eyes were wide open. "Clouds. I can see big white clouds."

John Smith took a small boat to the beach. He climbed to the top of a hill to get a good look at the land. It was a beautiful place with mountains, forests, and rivers.

Pocahontas was hiding behind a rock. She could not believe her eyes. All her people had dark hair and dark eyes. But this man had yellow hair and blue eyes. And his face seemed a strange color. His clothes were strange, too.

She ran back to the village and told her father everything.

Chief Powhatan said, "We must know more about these people. Kekata, what do you see?"

Kekata went to the fire and began to sing quietly. Then he took something from his bag and threw it into the smoke.

"These men are different from us. They wear metal uniforms that shine. They carry sticks that make fire. They are hungry animals, and they eat everything in their path."

"Chief Powhatan, we will kill these animals," Kocoum said.

"No Kocoum, we do not know how to fight them. Take some men and watch them. Perhaps they are not going to stay."

"Go and look for Indians," Ratcliffe said to John Smith. "If you see any, kill them!"

Ratcliffe turned to the sailors. "OK, men. Start digging!"

"Digging?" they replied.

"Yes, digging! What did the Spanish find in the new land? Gold, mountains of it! Now it's our turn. This time tomorrow, we will have more gold than the King of Spain! So dig, boys, dig!"

The sailors were excited and started digging fast. "There's enough gold for everyone. We'll be rich men!"

John Smith walked into the forest. The land was beautiful. He felt happy and excited. He stopped at a river to drink. Then suddenly, out of the corner of his eye, he saw something. A person! Someone was hiding in the trees. Was he in danger?

He walked along the river, then turned a corner. He hid behind a waterfall. He could see the person through it. With his gun in his hand, Smith jumped through the waterfall. He could not believe his eyes. He was looking at a beautiful woman. He put down his gun and moved toward her.

She ran.

"Wait, please!" he cried. He followed her. "I'm not going to hurt you," he said. She did not understand. She spoke to him. He did not understand.

Then slowly, Pocahontas took his hand and felt something deep inside her. The spirits of the forest moved around her. She remembered the words of Grandmother Willow, "Listen with your heart and you will understand." The spirits became stronger. Suddenly, she understood what the strange man was trying to say.

"Wait. Who are you?" he asked.

"Pocahontas. My name is Pocahontas." She could speak, too.

"I'm John Smith," the man said.

Kocoum led his men to a place above the river. They could see the sailors below.

"There are more than a hundred of them," said Kocoum.

"But what are they doing? Why are they digging?" asked his friend.

Suddenly, one of the sailors looked up and saw them. "Indians! Get your guns!" he shouted.

Ratcliffe's men started shooting and Kocoum and the others shot back with arrows. Suddenly, a bullet from Ratcliffe's gun hit one of Kocoum's men in the leg.

"To the village!" Kocoum shouted to the others. He picked up his friend and carried him on his back.

"These people are animals!" Chief Powhatan said when the men returned to the village. "They have come to our land, and they are shooting our people. We will fight them."

"But how can we fight them? There are too many of them, and they are strong."

"We cannot do it alone. We will call our brothers in the other villages. They will help us." Chief Powhatan looked carefully at the faces in front of him. "These white men are dangerous. Stay away from them. Do not go near them."

John Smith needed to see Pocahontas again. He knew that he loved her. Nothing else was important.

He found Pocahontas with her friend Nakoma. "I must see you, Pocahontas," he said.

She was glad to see him, too. "I must go, Nakoma," she told her friend. "Please don't say anything."

"But Pocahontas, it's dangerous! Remember your father's words!"

Suddenly, they heard a voice. "Pocahontas! Where are you?"

"It's Kocoum!" said Pocahontas. "We must go. Please, Nakoma, please?"

She and John Smith left.

"Nakoma. Have you seen Pocahontas?" asked Kocoum.

"Er ... no ... she's not here," replied Nakoma.

"Your land is so beautiful, Pocahontas," said John Smith. "But Ratcliffe and the others are here for one thing – gold."

"Gold? What's that?" Pocahontas asked.

"It's yellow. It comes from the ground. People like it very much."

"Oh! We have a lot of gold here," she said. She put her hand into her bag. "Here it is. It grows everywhere."

John Smith laughed. "No, that's not gold. This is gold." He gave her a gold coin.

Pocahontas looked at it carefully. "No, we don't have gold here."

"Ratcliffe and the men will be very unhappy," he said.

Just then, there was a strange noise.

"What was that?" he asked.

"Hello, John Smith."

John looked up. His eyes opened wide. "Is that tree talking to me, Pocahontas?"

"Don't be afraid, young man. Come closer. Let me see you. Hmmm ... Pocahontas, he's a good man, and handsome!"

John Smith heard the voices of his men. "I have to go, Pocahontas. Meet me here tonight."

"Perhaps he's your dream, child," Grandmother Willow said.

"Do you think the arrow in my dream was pointing me to him?"

Grandmother Willow smiled. "Yes, I do, my child. Yes, I do."

"We will kill the Indians, all of them!" Ratcliffe said.

"You can't do that," replied John Smith. "We don't have to fight them. I met one of them. They're not bad. They can help us. And there is no gold. There's only this plant — and it's food!"

"No gold?" the men said.

"Did your friend tell you this?" Ratcliffe shouted at John Smith. "There IS gold. They just want to keep it all for themselves!"

"But it's their land," said John Smith.

"It is MY land," cried Ratcliffe. "And I say that all the Indians will die!"

Pocahontas ran through the forest to meet John Smith.

Nakoma ran after her. "Pocahontas! Don't go. It is wrong!" she cried.

"No, Nakoma, I know this is right. I am doing this for my people."

"I kept your secret before. I won't do it again," Nakoma said angrily.

"I have to do this," said Pocahontas, and she ran away.

Nakoma worried about her friend. She had to tell Kocoum. She ran to find him.

"Kocoum, it's Pocahontas ..." she said.

"What's wrong?" he cried. "Is she all right?"

"I think she's in trouble," said Nakoma. Then she told him everything.

That night, John Smith left to meet Pocahontas. Thomas saw him leave.

A quiet voice said to Thomas, "Follow him, boy. Do not lose him." It was Ratcliffe. "I want to know everything. And if you see an Indian, kill him!"

Thomas followed. It was difficult moving through the forest. Then John Smith stopped. Thomas could not believe his eyes. A beautiful Indian woman came out of the trees and walked into John Smith's arms.

Now Thomas understood, but he was afraid for his friend. This meeting was very dangerous.

"Pocahontas, my men are going to attack your people. You must tell them," John Smith said quickly.

"We have to stop this. It will be terrible and many people will die," she replied. "You must come and speak to my father."

"That won't help. Talking won't change anything."

"Young man," said Grandmother Willow, "sometimes the right path is not easy. You want to be together. So there must be peace between your peoples."

"All right, let's talk to your father," John Smith agreed.

He looked into Pocahontas's eyes — and they kissed.

From behind a tree, Kocoum saw the kiss.

He jumped out with a large knife in his hand. He shouted loudly and ran at John Smith. He wanted to kill this stranger!

John Smith fought hard, but Kocoum was too strong and fast. He threw the Englishman to the ground and held the knife to his neck.

Thomas knew that he had to save his friend. He held up the gun and breathed deeply. Then he shot.

Kocoum fell to the ground. He was dead!

"Get out of here, Thomas!" shouted John Smith. Thomas ran.

Kocoum's brothers heard the gun and ran to the old tree. They took John Smith by the arms and dragged him back to the village.

"Who did this?" cried Chief Powhatan.

"Pocahontas was in the forest. Kocoum went to find her. Then this stranger attacked him."

"You have killed a brave man. When the sun comes up in the morning, you will die!" shouted Chief Powhatan.

"But, Father ..." cried Pocahontas.

"You went outside the village against my orders. Now Kocoum is dead. You are a bad daughter!" he shouted.

"Oh, Nakoma, I'll never see him again," Pocahontas said to her friend.

"Yes, you will. Come with me." Nakoma led her friend to a tent. There were guards outside.

"This man killed Kocoum. Pocahontas wants to look into his eyes," Nakoma told them.

Pocahontas went in. There was a rope around John Smith's hands. He looked sad, but he smiled at Pocahontas.

"I'm sorry, John," she said.

"Don't be sorry. I will die a happy man because I have known you."

"I can't leave you," she said.

He looked into her eyes. "I will always be with you."

Pocahontas sat in front of Grandmother Willow. "They're going to kill him in the morning."

"You have to stop them," replied Grandmother Willow. "Remember your dream."

"No, I followed the wrong path. I feel so lost."

Suddenly, she saw something. It was shining. It was a compass. She looked at it. There was an arrow! It was moving!

"It's the arrow from your dream," Grandmother Willow said.

"I was right," smiled Pocahontas. "He *is* the right path!"

"It's not too late," said Grandmother Willow. "The spirits will lead you! You know your path, child. Now follow it!"

In the morning, Ratcliffe and his men marched toward the village to fight the Indians. Chief Powhatan and his men marched toward the river to fight the Englishmen. But first, they wanted to kill John Smith.

Pocahontas ran as fast as possible to save John Smith.

"No, Father, stop!" cried Pocahontas, and she threw herself over John Smith. "If you kill him, you have to kill me, too."

"Daughter, stand back," said Chief Powhatan.

"No. I love him, Father."

Her father's mouth fell open.

She continued. "We must not fight — it is the wrong path."

Her father looked around. Perhaps Pocahontas was right. He looked far across the mountains and breathed deeply. There was a sweet smell in the air. He felt the spirits of the forest and the wind.

"My daughter is right. We have all come here with anger in our hearts. But she is brave, and comes with love. We will not fight. Let the stranger go." His men put down their arrows and the sailors put down their guns.

Pocahontas and John Smith kissed.

But Ratcliffe was angry. "Now, men, shoot them!" he shouted.
The Englishmen did not move. He picked up a gun and pointed it
at Chief Powhatan.

John Smith jumped in front of Pocahontas's father. There was a
loud noise and John Smith fell to the ground.

"John!" cried Thomas.

"You shot him! We'll never listen to you again," shouted Thomas
at Ratcliffe. "Take him, men!" he shouted to the others.

They took away Ratcliffe's gun. Then they dragged him back to
the ship. There, they put ropes around him and locked him in a
small room.

The sailors carried John Smith to the river.

"I hope he lives," said one of them.

"The ship's almost ready. We need to go now," Thomas said to John Smith.

"No, not yet. She'll be here, I'm sure," John said.

Then, Pocahontas came out of the trees. Other Indians came with her. They brought gifts for the sailors. They brought food to help them on their journey.

John Smith was lying on the ground near the water.

"We must take him back to England. He'll die here," Thomas told Pocahontas.

She touched his arm, then walked slowly toward John Smith.

"You are always welcome here," Chief Powhatan said to John Smith. "Thank you for saving my life, my brother." He smiled.

Pocahontas sat down next to the man she loved.

John Smith looked deep into her eyes. "Come with me?"

She looked at her father.

"You must decide your path, my daughter," he said to her.

Pocahontas looked toward the forest, then at the faces of her people. She turned slowly back to John Smith and took his hand. She held it against her face. "My place is here."

"I'll stay here with you," John Smith said.

"No, you have to go back."

"But I can't leave you."

"You never will. I'll always be with you," Pocahontas said.

She touched his face softly and he put his arm around her. They kissed for one last time. Then the sailors picked up John Smith and carried him toward the ship. John Smith waved and tried to smile. It was difficult. They were deeply sad. But they knew that he had to leave. And they knew, too, that she had to stay.

The sailors put John Smith into a small boat and took him out to the ship. Pocahontas and her father watched. Their hearts were heavy because John Smith was leaving. He was a good man and a true friend to his men and to them.

The sailors prepared the ship. Soon it was moving slowly along the river toward the open ocean.

Pocahontas left her father's side and ran along the land beside the ship. She ran as fast as the wind. Then she climbed to a high rock.

From there, she could see the ship below. John Smith looked up from his bed and saw her. She looked so beautiful with the wind in her hair. He could see something else, too. The spirits of the forest seemed to be all around her.

Pocahontas sent her love to John Smith from the bottom of her heart.

On the ship, John Smith smiled. He felt the spirits of the land and the love from Pocahontas. He loved her, too.

And the ship sailed slowly toward the open ocean.

Before You Read

❶ **What do you know about the story of Pocahontas? What can you see in this picture?** *shipccoy*

❷ **Look quickly through the book. Match the names with these people a–f.**

1 Chief Powhatan
2 Ratcliffe
3 Kocoum
4 John Smith
5 Pocahontas
6 Nakoma

After You Read

❶ Who are these sentences about: John Smith or Pocahontas or both?

a My home is in a city. _____John Smith_____

b My home is in the forest. _____Pocahontas_____

c I have to stay with my people. _Pocahontas_

d I have to leave. _JohnSmith_

e I am a sailor. _John Smith_

f I am the daughter of the Chief. _Pocahontas_

g I will always be with you. _Pocahontas_

❷ Finish these sentences.

1 Kocoum wanted to marry _Pocahontas_

a Nakoma.   b Pocahontas.   c a girl from England.

2 Pocahontas thought the ship looked like _clouds_

a trees.   b a river.   c clouds.

3 The smoke in the fire tells Kekata that the strangers are _dangerous_

a friendly.   b dangerous.   c sick.

4 The sailors have never seen _corn_ before.

a corn   b gold   c ships

5 _the co mpass_ tells Pocahontas that John Smith is the right man for her.

a Kekata   b Ratcliffe   c The compass

❸ Talk about these questions in groups.

a Why did the Indians want to kill John Smith? Were they right, do you think?

b Why did Ratcliffe want to kill the Indians? Was he right, do you think?